IT'S GREEN AGAIN

South Wales ECHO

IT'S *GREN* AGAIN

A COLLECTION OF SOME OF HIS FAVOURITE CARTOONS

breedon **books** PUBLISHING

First published in Great Britain in 2001 by
The Breedon Books Publishing Company Limited
Breedon House, 3 The Parker Centre, Derby, DE21 4SZ.

ISBN 1 85983 241 5

Printed by Butler & Tanner, Frome, Somerset, England.

Cover printing by Lawrence-Allen, Avon, England.

Contents

CHAPTER ONE

Cartoons from the South Wales Echo and Wales on Sunday

Gren has been producing a daily cartoon for the *South Wales Echo* for over 30 years and for *Wales On Sunday* for the past 10 years. The following is a very small selection of that vast output, which indicates the wide range of news items that have attracted his humour.

The Olympics begin and we are told it will be a triumph of television.

'See you two weeks on Sunday then.'
(24 July 1992)

The Pope is admitted to hospital for surgery.

'Next time ask him to take it off!'
(13 July 1992)

An aircraft accidentally drops a bomb on its own ship – the *Ark Royal.*

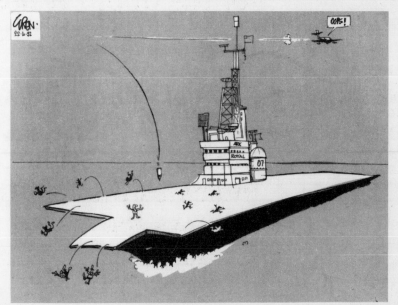

'Don't panic lads – it's one of ours!'
(22 April 1992)

Princess Anne and Mark are to divorce.

'He gets to see us every weekend.'
(14 April 1992)

Boxer Mike Tyson is at the centre of a long-running American court case.

'And for the latest on the Tyson trial, over to Harry Carpenter at the courtside...'
(10 February 1992)

WRU squad are told to wear Adidas equipment at all times.

'Sometimes I wish you'd never got in the ruddy squad.'
(28 December 1984)

Video nasties are often shown as entertainment at children's birthday parties.

'Which colour jelly would you like, Chain Saw Massacre Red, the Sex Crazed Creature from the Swamp Green or Driller Killer Yellow?'
(24 November 1983)

The Greenham Common women are getting a lot of press attention.

'She doesn't actually go to Greenham Common, but she does support them.'
(23 November 1983)

Airline food is criticised by Egon Ronay.

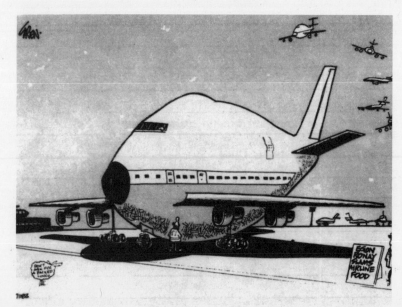

'We're still too overloaded to take off – I'm afraid we'll have to jettison the bread pudding.'
(7 November 1983)

Fourteen new prisons are to be built.

'I see they're going to build fourteen new prisons.'
(22 November 1983)

The Americans invade Grenada.

'Hold it – apparently the Yanks have invaded Grenada, not...'
(26 October 1983)

Neil Kinnock becomes Labour Party leader.

'There are going to be a couple of changes – instead of the Red Flag we're doing Sospan Fach…'
(3 October 1983)

There was a mass escape at the Maze Prison, Belfast.

'Hang on missus, I'll see if he's in.'
(28 September 1983)

The British team entered in the Americas Cup are anxious about the Australians' 'secret' keel design.

'As I said to the Aussies and the Yanks – if you can have secret keel modifications, so can we!'
(1 September 1983)

A big fiddle was uncovered where Chanel perfume was being made in a backstreet garage.

'As usual they made one fatal mistake.'
(19 August 1983)

Wimbledon begins. Offending players will be dealt with severely.

'I hope they give him a chance and don't prejudge the issue.'
(22 June 1984)

Maggie Thatcher isn't too pleased about a portrait which makes her look slightly cross-eyed.

'He didn't take her criticism as badly as I first thought he would.'
(21 June 1984)

The European Parliament elections seem to hold little interest for most people.

'I was going to speak on apathy...'
(13 June 1984)

Reagan in Ireland looks up his supposed family in a vote-catching deal.

'So much for the Irish-American vote – now for the Pennsylvanian-Welsh.'
(4 June 1984)

The South Glamorgan Ambulance Service is unable to operate fully because of serious defects to its ambulances.

'Know anything about releasing a seized wheel bearing...?'
(18 May 1984)

The South Glamorgan Ambulance Service is having to take a lot of its fleet off the road due to defects.

'He was only coming in to have his boil lanced when the ambulance wheel fell on his foot.'
(18 June 1984)

Miners' wives, supporting their striking husbands, are arrested for obstruction.

'Quick, Bert's buying – they've arrested his wife too!'
(10 May 1984)

Torville and Dean dominate our screens with their incredible routines.

'Oy, Dad – Ravel and Bolero are on again.'
(27 March 1984)

NUM pickets are very active.

'There's a story going around that MacGregor wants to close it.'
(23 March 1984)

Flying pickets are everywhere.

'He's not much cop on the coalface – but he's a fantastic flying picket.'
(22 March 1984)

Men came out of a survey very badly.

'Ere Glad, luv, read this to me.'
(16 February 1984)

TV license dodgers face £400 in fines.

'And this one madam, tells you if there's a detector van in your area.'
(21 February 1984)

The Winter Olympics are here again.

'I like this one, it always annoys the Austrians.'
(9 February 1984)

Mark Thatcher's involvement in a contract awarded to Cementation Ltd is criticised.

'Me too, I don't care what her conditions were as long as the shipyard gets the business.'
(31 January 1984)

Editors are asked to give Charles and Di peace on their winter sports holiday.

'Fair's fair, my editor didn't promise we wouldn't take pictures – he promised not to harass them on the slopes.'
(9 January 1984)

Whitbread the brewers announce a scheme whereby they contribute to a charity for each barrel sold in the pubs.

'You can be proud of your Cyril – he's been working for charity all night.'
(16 September 1986)

The annual Children in Need Appeal is on TV. Again the viewers are wonderfully generous.

'I think Nana's been at the sherry again – she's just bid £20,000 for Terry Wogan.'
(21 November 1987)

A dinosaur exhibition opens at the National Museum of Wales.

'Here Rover, good boy Rover.'
(18 November 1986)

Scientists equipped with sonar equipment failed to find the Loch Ness Monster.

'Ah well, that's it. We've put an end to the legend – there's nothing down there.'
(17 October 1987)

There were allegations regarding the misuse of drugs during the Rome games.

'And when he comes down, do a drugs test.'
(7 September 1987)

The Prince and Princess of Wales are holidaying in Majorca.

'Oh, him. He time shares castles!'
(13 August 1986)

Welshman Timothy Dalton is to be the new James Bond.

'S4C here. Look – ever thought of remaking all the old ones?'
(8 August 1986)

Suggestions are invited to name the new bridge over the Severn.

'Thank you Mr Kinnock, we'll let you know.'
(7 August 1986)

Aled Jones is to retire before his voice breaks.

'...and here to sing Old Man River is...'
(6 January 1987)

The show must go on – Michael Crawford ignores the pain of his hiatus hernia to perform in *Phantom of the Opera*.

'I see pain-killing injections are by Pollack and Johnstone.'
(23 July 1987)

The government has agreed to back councils that fine owners of dogs who misbehave.

'The council were thinking more of "owners of dogs fouling will be fined".'
(8 April 1987)

The *QE2* has been plagued by troubles since its recent overhaul.

'Now you may be wondering why the engines are running so quietly...'
(1 May 1987)

Clint Eastwood becomes Mayor of Carmel.

'For heaven's sake Idwal, can't you forget about standing for the local council?'
(10 April 1986)

It's Grand National day.

'You remember, same one as last year – nice-looking boy, green and pink shirt on a brown horse.'
(4 April 1987)

A report about health foods includes crisps as beneficial.

'Today I starta sella da crispa too!'
(11 March 1986)

The Mona Lisa is a self-portrait of Leonardo, claims an art expert.

'So if you don't mind Mr Da Vinci, until you've finished I'll bring your drinks up – you're giving the place a bad name.'
(1 March 1987)

The English tactics were 'questionable' against Wales in the Arms Park international.

The Admiral's Cup races are underway.

'I think the skipper would like a word with you Arnold.'
(2 February 1987)

Hedgehog flavoured crisps are launched.

(8 February 1984)

As Christmas approaches a flu epidemic rages through Wales.

(9 December 1988)

The Welsh company Peter's Pies has been sold for £75 million.

'It's just – when you said my blind date was a pie man – I naturally hoped...'
(10 November 1988)

Drug-taking to improve athletes' performance is in the news.

'I'd often suspected something fishy – but until this week I'd never even heard of anabolic steroids.'
(29 September 1988)

Joan Collins quits *Dynasty* – will the marvellous *Pobol-y-Cwm* make a bid for her services?

'Here's how I see it. Alexis moves in, and by the second episode she's seduced the vicar, organist, policeman and half the choir.'
(18 May 1989)

Suggestion that the National Stadium should be moved to allow the valuable space to be used for yet more office accommodation.

'So then they came to a compromise.'
(7 June 1989)

Oh, the shame of it all. The rugby posts at the National Stadium are removed for the Wales v West Germany soccer game.

'No, honestly. They'll go back in September.'
(10 May 1989)

A lottery to aid NHS funds is proposed.

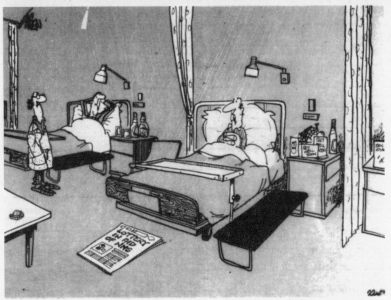

'It seemed a pity not to take advantage of it. I won this free haemorrhoids operation...'
(22 April 1988)

Ian Botham is to be part of a fund-raising event in which he becomes Hannibal of 1988. The money raised will go to leukaemia research.

'This is easy. Ever tried the last bus to Ely on Saturdays?'
(28 March 1988)

Tom Jones is to buy a home in the Vale of Glamorgan.

'So far my client's impressed – now what are the acoustics like in the bathroom?'
(25 April 1989)

Eddie 'The Eagle' Edwards is due to jump today at the Winter Olympics.

'I see Eddie's got another sponsor.'
(22 February 1988)

Soft cheese is alive with bacteria say the experts.

'Myrtle won't be long – she's just killing the cheese!'
(15 February 1989)

Yet another attempt to extradite Ronnie Knight is made.

'Ere Ronnie it's for you, something about a time share in Britain.'
(22 February 1989)

Brie is the latest in the line of horror-story foods.

'Who was it wanted a pound of Brie?'
(13 February 1989)

A plan is announced by the Secretary of State for Wales which should transform the Welsh Valleys.

'Straight on to the proposed helicopter pad, right at the proposed monorail terminal, left at the proposed six-star hotel, and the Bracchi's on your left.'   *(12 January 1988)*

A public debate on the Cardiff barrage proposals is demanded by anxious Grangetown residents.

'And here to speak on behalf of the residents of Grangetown...'
(3 January 1989)

Hirohito's funeral: much debate about whether Britain should be represented at all, let alone by the Duke of Edinburgh.

'My Ronald doesn't know if he should go. He was in Singapore during the war, but on the other hand he's got a Toyota.'
(5 January 1989)

Eddie 'The Eagle' Edwards is injured in a ski-jump fall.

'Oh yes, you can't miss him – fourth on the right.'
(4 January 1989)

More health food scares – it seems whatever we eat is out to get us.

'What do you fancy for supper – salmonella or listeria?'
(13 January 1989)

The shortage of NHS nurses in Wales is of crisis proportions.

'When you've finished here Vera, could you do a few injections on ward 10?' *(3 January 1999)*

After much criticism that Shirley Bassey was only miming at the Millennium Stadium during the Rugby World Cup opening ceremony, she is made in wax for exhibition at Madame Tussaud's.

'Can you make it look a bit more like she's miming?' *(18 November 1999)*

The Christmas story is told many times against news stories of Lord Mayor Russell Goodway and his huge salary and expenses.

'I hope it doesn't turn out to be Russell Goodway – we couldn't afford him.' *(24 December 1999)*

Heavy rains lead to widespread flooding in many parts of Wales.

'Mine's the same – funny woman. Always wanted a water feature in the garden, now she's got one she's still not satisfied!' *(1 November 1998)*

It's Wales v Argentina at the Millennium Stadium.

'And finally boys, try to wind them up, tell them their corned beef is rubbish!'
(1 October 1999)

The TV quiz show *Who Wants To Be A Millionaire?* is a big talking point.

'Can I phone a friend?"'
(8 September 1999)

Hard-man Vinny Jones is reported to be wanting to buy a football club.

'Vinny's very interested – he's been here and says he likes the feel of the club.'
(30 August 1999)

Genetically-modified crops are sabotaged by anti-GM food groups.

(19 August 1999)

The morning-after pill will be available over the counter.

'I'm worried, do you have a two weeks last Tuesday morning-after pill?'
(1 August 1999)

Golfers are told to beware of snakes in the heatwave.

'Rhodri was having a good round till that boa constrictor got him on the fourteenth.'
(14 July 1999)

There are claims that members of the European Parliament are turning it into a gravy train.

'Well he'll get my vote, he's refreshingly honest.'
(9 June 1999)

Ginger Spice quits the Spice Girls – much to the concern of many of their fans.

'There, there, darling. Grampy understands just how you feel – I was just the same when Barry John decided to quit the game!'
(2 June 1998)

A new-style, longer driving test is announced.

'If you don't find reverse this time Miss Pugh, I'm afraid I'm going to have to fail you.'
(5 May 1999)

It's official, the minimum wage has been settled at £3.60.

'I've been giving my wife more than that – £5 a week and she's still moaning.'
(6 April 1999)

Pets are going to be allowed to accompany their owners on overseas visits.

'He's ever so excited about it – he's never been to Benidorm before.'
(31 March 1999)

The row over Southern Hemisphere rugby internationals claiming Welsh grandparents is big news.

'Just to be on the safe side N'tanga. Would you be happy to change your name to N'tanga N'tanga Umbo Ap Tomos?'
(28 March 2000)

Welsh coach Graham Henry is expected to put Welsh rugby back on a winning streak very soon.

'Next, little Dewi will recite his own charming little poem about what he would do if he were Graham Henry.'
(1 March 1999)

St David's Day coincides with the rumpus in Welsh rugby over players wearing the red jersey because of claimed Welsh grandparents.

'Please sir, he came over from Australia or New Zealand, and probably got the job because he had a Welsh grandfather.'
(1 March 2000)

A Welsh Tartan is unveiled with great publicity.

'No, no, Mansel bach! The kilt I don't mind, but bloody bagpipes – no way.'
(25 February 2000)

Catherine Zeta Jones announces that she is pregnant.

'Mumsy, daddy – the doctors think I'm Zeta'd!'
(2 February 2000)

There was a lovely story doing the rounds that Catherine Zeta Jones and Michael Douglas were going to marry in Wales.

'And if Catherine Zeta Jones phones back, yes we can do a reception for 60 if the pub team aren't using the skittle alley.'
(17 January 2000)

Shock, horror! It's announced that Brains are to close their Cardiff brewery.

'I thought they were closing – I didn't know they were going to continue brewing just across the river.'
(12 January 1999)

Cardiff and County Club still continues to refuse membership to all ladies.

'You should have said you didn't like the vicar's mucky jokes and foul language before I managed to fiddle your membership... Cynthia.'
(15 January 1999)

There are many news stories about overcrowded wards in our hospitals.

'Frankly, with hindsight, I preferred my trolley in the corridor.'
(11 January 1999)

Catherine Zeta Jones and Michael Douglas announce their intention to marry.

'We were just sayin' to the women, we don't know what she sees in him – I bet he doesn't know a damn thing about rugby!'
(8 January 2000)

The Euro is still making the headlines.

'I'll never understand it – I still don't know how many Euros there are to the litre!'
(6 January 1999)

Britain pulls out of UNESCO.

'Relax! UNESCO not Tesco!'
(6 December 1985)

The Sunday trading laws are criticised by many bodies, including the Church.

'As I was coming here this morning via B&Q...'
(7 November 1985)

An explosion at a Cardiff curry house causes problems in the city centre.

'Now that's what I call a curry.'
(29 October 1985)

The Pill may be prescribed for under-age girls.

'Remember the old days when it was Reds versus Blues?'
(8 October 1985)

Some wine that is coming into the country is contaminated with an antifreeze-type solution.

'...An impetuous little wine, slightly frivolous, yet delicately seductive – and it also protects your radiator.'
(26 July 1985)

There are complaints that Welsh speakers are queue-jumping in the search for jobs.

'...Same here, only got the job because I had the language.'
(17 July 1985)

A potato glut leads to an all-time low price per pound.

'The wife should have been more specific really... instead of just asking them to just deliver a few quids worth of spuds.'
(11 July 1985)

Bob Geldof has harnessed everyone's energy in a charity direction – well almost everyone.

'We can't run – and don't like pop music, but we'd still like to help.'
(26 May 1986)

The last coal from the Rhondda Valley was raised yesterday.

(1 July 1986)

Euro Disney advertise for staff.

'Try to remember to mention it. Idwal managed to get a job today.'
(21 January 1992)

The English team reach the semi-final of cricket's World Cup, with very few fit players.

'And he's bowling to a field of two dodgy hamstrings, a rib cartilage, a strained thigh and several pulled muscles.'
(17 March 1992)

A pilot suffered a fatal heart attack while flying over South Wales. His inexperienced co-pilot was talked down successfully by an instructor flying nearby.

'That Welsh pilot certainly started something.'
(1 April 1992)

Frank Bruno gets back into the ring after a very successful panto season.

'A lot of Bruno's panto fans are here tonight.'

A leading government minister complains about *Neighbours,* saying it's a load of rubbish.

'I'm worried about the effect it's having on your mother too.'
(14 May 1991)

The *South Wales Echo* becomes the major sponsor of Cardiff City AFC.

'...And the fair-haired ex-gas fitter, father-of-two, lays the ball off to surprised former spot-welder Lewis, 25, of Roath who...'
(12 June 1992)

Legal moves begin over Sunday trading.

'Today's lesson is taken from chapter five of the Sunday Trading Laws.'
(6 July 1992)

Gazza's injury is grabbing lots of headlines.

'Your career isn't necessarily over Gazza. Adidas are bringing out a range of crutches, and they were wondering...'
(10 October 1991)

The Pavarotti in the Park concert at Hyde Park was a great success.

'Hey Luciano baby, thata lasta notea, whata da beauty.'
(30 July 1991)

McDonalds and Salisbury Cathedral strike up a sponsorship deal.

'Frankly I think this sponsorship thing has gone too far.'
(12 August 1992)

The RAF is on stand-by to fly to the Gulf.

'Can you hang on a bit? Kate Adie's not quite ready.'
(18 August 1992)

MP David Mellor is said to have liked making love wearing Chelsea AFC strip.

'No thank you dear – not tonight, I've got a headache.'
(8 September 1992)

The teaching of English must improve, schools are instructed.

'I see you're getting through to 3B.'
(10 September 1992)

35

A report says women get an unfair deal when it comes to hours worked.

'Try an' keep quiet in there, I'm trying to read this.'
(25 September 1991)

A wheel drops off Mansell's car during a big race.

'Nigel always likes to do his own pre-race checks.'
(23 September 1991)

Corn circles are said to be the results of a gigantic hoax.

'According to this here, it's all one big hoax.'
(9 September 1991)

New kerb-crawling laws are announced.

'It's not so much the job I don't like – it's just everyone calling me a kerb crawler.'
(4 October 1991)

Welsh Rugby fans are not exactly overjoyed at having to watch a World Cup Final between Australia and England.

'All right then, can I watch if I promise not to cheer Australia or England?'
(1 November 1991)

The new 'M' is a lady.

'I've been trying to decode it for two days – I've only just realised it's her knitting pattern.'
(17 December 1991)

Supermarkets are flouting the Sunday Trading Laws.

'It's a mixed marriage – he's Asda Baptist, and she's strict Methodist Tesco.'
(2 December 1991)

Andrew Lloyd-Webber pays a fortune for a very famous Canaletto painting.

'No! no! no! I said go out and buy me a Cornetto.'
(16 April 1992)

Yet another hi-tech Nessie hunt at Loch Ness is announced.

'You'd think by now they wouldn't warn us when they're coming.'
(14 July 1992)

The actions of Fergie are reported to have angered the Queen.

'You can't fool me Elizabeth, you're a trifle fraught aren't you?'
(20 March 1992)

CHAPTER TWO

Ponty an' Pop —The everyday story of Aberflyarff folk

Ponty an' Pop has appeared in the sports editions of the *South Wales Echo* for 25 years.

The strip is about the rugby-mad village of Royal Aberflyarff where the rugby-nutter inhabitants discuss every WRU pronouncement and the ups and downs of the rugby scene.

At the local pub, the Golden Dap, regulars are welcomed by lovely Bromide Lil, barmaid, part-time sex goddess and sometime model for oven gloves.

In addition to gracing the pages of the *Sports Echo*, Ponty an' Pop has been broadcast on radio and seen on TV, with leading parts being played by Owen Money, Frank Henessey, Tommy David and Caryl Parry-Jones.

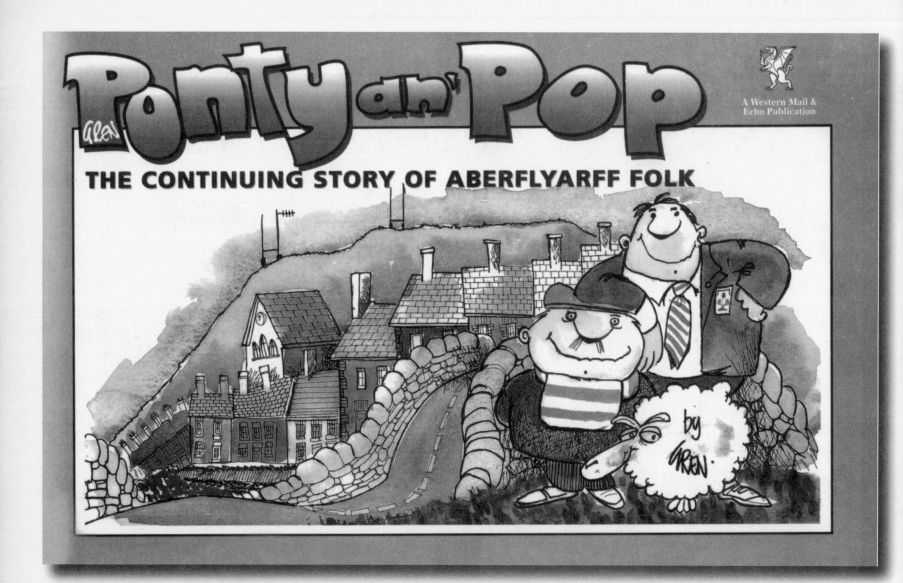

Ponty - is Mr Aberflyarff RFC, he's the club chairman, the secretary and he is also responsible for team selection and sending reports of the team's latest game to the local press.
An ex-Aberflyarff player who would give his life for the club (unless he had a better offer from Cardiff). He and **Pop** are co-authors of 'Aberflyarff RFC - The Glory Years'.

Pop is now full-time unemployed, he lost his job at Aberflyarff's Japanese factory when hi-tech came in - he wasn't replaced by a computer, he was replaced by a pocket calculator.

Nigel is the head groundsman at Aberflyarff's Sir Waldo Trahernia Sportsdome, a position he has held since giving up the game in 1980. He will always be remembered for that occasion in an Aberflyarff - England game when Will Carling, with no one to beat, the line at his mercy, twenty yards out, fell over him! And Aberflyarff went on to thrash England 3-Nil.

Bromide Lil - darling barmaid of the Golden Dap. Still a part-time sex symbol and model for welding gloves and pit boots. She and Ponty were once engaged - this was broken off as soon as she had the ring valued. Lil will do almost anything for a North stand ticket.

Arnold Nutstrampler - Still club captain after all these years, a player who is a fine example to all the up and coming youth thugs. Arnold still holds the WRU record for infringements in one game (104) and sendings off during one season (97). He has made the position of loosehead provoker his own since 1975. This is his benefit season, as long as they can get Owen Money and Dai Vaughan for the dinner.

Ronald the Ref
Very sad case is Ronald, he played for Royal Aberflyarff for nearly nineteen glorious years before his pace went and his eyesight failed and due to age he began to forget the rules.
It will come as no surprise to Rugby lovers everywhere that Ronald did the usual thing.
Yes, he became a ref.

Attila Groinstomper is the club's open-side groiner. He has been watched by Welsh Selectors, Lions Selectors and Special Branch. This is Attila's tenth season at Aberflyarff where he is in hiding from the Child Support Agency.

Bleddyn - the club's security investment . Trained to go for the legs of any marauding league or union scout, also the legs of visiting backs with the line at their mercy.

Like all top clubs Royal Aberflyarff RFC needs sponsorship to survive…

The start of the season is always an exciting time as optimistic plans are made...

The Welsh XV performed well at Twickenham, narrowly losing to a much fancied England side.

Jonathan Davies plays his first game for Cardiff, and it did appear that the other 14 players wouldn't pass the ball to him.

It's time once more to follow our glorious team to Ireland for the Five Nations game...

A bid for the new National Stadium to be built at Bridgend, not Cardiff, has been announced.

Kevin Bowring is named as new Coaching Director.

It's BBC Wales Sports Personality of the Year time again.

Clubs are now offering huge playing fees. Will Royal Aberflyarff have to follow suit?

Rugby friendships last forever — or so it is believed.

Most clubs now boast a 'youth policy'. So too at Royal Aberflyarff…

CHAPTER THREE

Gren's Rugby Addicts calendar

The Rugby Addicts calendar was first published in 1969 and has been produced annually ever since. The cartoons reflect a rugby way of life and the lovely nutters that surround the game.

'I'd move tomorrow, but my husband loves it here!'

'Ignore it boys — they're just trying to put us off!'

'I don't know who Age Concern are — but they've seen us play and have offered us a sponsorship deal.'

'He's decided to play to our strengths this week. He's picked another two psychos, an assassin and a blindside nutter.'

'Ere Glad, can you squeeze into size 10 boots and do you know anything about drift defence — we're one short.'

'Marvellous innit — only once every two years we play England at the Arms Park, an' she would insist.'

'I still say if it wasn't for his lousy sense of direction he'd have had a cap by now!'

'Well I've never seen that before, a tackle bag retaliating!'

'Right lads! Get out there and don't forget — never bite anyone who hasn't had a tetanus jab!'

'You're worried about her being late, how d'you think the groom feels, he's kicking off in an hour?'

'Having explosive acceleration is all very well, as long as you have a similar thing in deceleration!'

'Frankly, I'm surprised it wasn't called off.'

'I hate these players who haven't been ruined by alcohol or women yet.'

'I think he's done you for not releasing it.'

CHAPTER 4

Welsh and proud of it

These cartoons are about Wales and the Welsh way of life. They are published annually in calendar form. In addition to being very popular within Wales they are sent to Welsh folk living all over the world to keep loved ones in touch with the ways of their country and their roots.

'And now, hymn one hundred and fifty-four — with all the Arms Park fervour you can muster.'

'It's Emrys the Druid — he's been sponsored!'

'I love it here, everyone's so friendly.'

'Next, little Harri will recite from the Mabinogion and then tell you where he thinks the WRU are going wrong.'

'I always thought he would have done better for himself after winning the Cardiff Singer of the World title.'

'It'll never work. It's a mixed marriage. He's from South Wales, she's from North!'

'996… 997… 998… 999! — Anyone seen Ianto?'

'Call that entertainment — been on half an hour and still haven't done Myfanwy!'

'Yes, but would you let your daughter marry one?'

'He only got the job because he was bilingual.'

'Sometimes I wish the Secretary of State for Wales wouldn't bother to come.'

'I don't like the place much — but my old man seems to be settling in quite nicely.'

'Considering he only came here once for a half of shandy, you're certainly making the most of it.'

'Okay, Brenda. Off you go and try and pitch the dramatic interpretation somewhere between Shirley Bassey and Charlotte Church.'

CHAPTER FIVE

Sporting Drawings

Being a keen sportsman, Gren is delighted to turn his attention to sport whenever asked to do so. The following are a few of his single-figure style drawings for various publications.

The moment the selectors decided to overlook me. 'You'd think they could overlook the odd mistake wouldn't you... Okay so my speed isn't that great... I may be lacking in ideas... but on the other hand I can read the game, I always know why we've lost... What do they expect, some public school whizz-kid who can actually understand the line-out laws? Please yourself mates... the wife wants me to pack it in anyway...'

(From the first Rugby Addicts calendar for the Funfare Press, 1969)

The moment I hated the selection committee.
'…they never did like me… too blind to appreciate my progressive style of play… ah well, if they want the kick and chase types, fair enough… don't let them come crawling back to me that's all… it would be a different story if I were related to someone on the selection committee, like most of the firsts are… oh yes, they never did like me…'

(From the first Rugby Addicts calendar for the Funfare Press, 1969)

Mark Sandspencer
Club captain and guiding light behind the team. His obvious class shows when he takes guard on a line of middle and box. He is a reliable middle order bat who can always be certain to get a regular eight or nine before being out due to amazing bad luck, i.e. 'Damn ball deflected by a sparrow', or 'I've never seen one come back four feet before.'
(From the Cricket Addicts calendar, 1970)

Lucy Tania

Let us remind you about Lucy Tania,
* her consuming passion was a bowling mania.*
Her style and her action were poetry in motion,
* each wood had bias and weight to perfection.*
Ladies, how well you may know Lucy's problem,
* the weight of her torso destroyed equilibrium.*
Each time she gracefully released her bowl,
* she wobbled and fell, and created a hole.*
Her teammates repeatedly dusted her down,
* but their game never prospered on such dented ground.*

(From a series of Sporting Heroes)

Justin Case

If Justin's the name, then snooker's the game,
surely this could be his way to great fame?
For 'Casey' the issue seemed quite simple,
since able to pot balls by the handful.
A youthful prospect, all seemed assured,
TV matches would soon be secured.
But how to explain to our budding professional
that naming the balls just isn't ethical.
Those late night sessions on the green baize
had Justin's vision all in a haze.
Yes, colour-blindness becomes a real pain
when red, blue and green all seem the same.

(From a series of Sporting Heroes)

The Boxer
(From a series of Sporting Heroes)

The Jogging Type

Jogging is a great excuse to get away from the wife while you jog to the nearest pub.

Joggers ignore the neighbours and their funny remarks – ignore the rabid dogs snapping at their heels, ignore the policeman who thinks the jogger is a runaway mugger, in the knowledge that the jog has done them some good – or at least would have done had it not been for those five pints and eight scotches needed at the pub to revive them after the jog.

(From a series of Sporting Heroes)

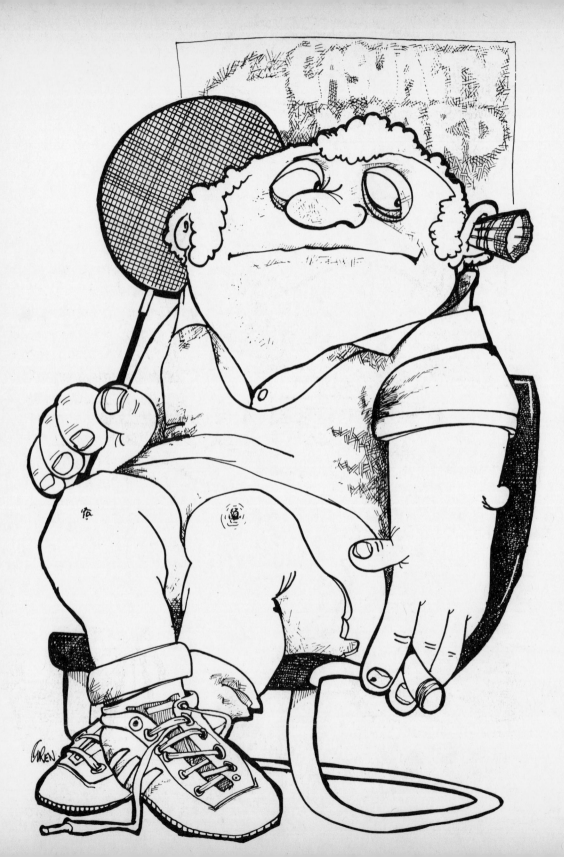

The Badminton Type

The Badminton Type is a Squash Type who can't run around any more. The nice thing about badminton is that if you hit the shuttlecock high enough you can take a quick smoke before your opponent knocks it back to you.

Another nice thing about badminton is that the shuttlecock never bounces away. Therefore you haven't got to walk far for it.

There are two good reasons for joining a badminton club:

1. The exercise will do you good.
2. The birds are usually quite dolly.

(From a series of Sporting Heroes)

The Golf Type

The Golf Type is to athletics what a hernia is to weightlifting.

Golf types talk endlessly about their last boring round during which their drives went further and straighter and their putting was perfect.

The rules for the real golf type are very simple: Never go out with less than a dozen balls and never ever beat your managing director.

There are three types of golfer:
1. 'It's only 400 yards – pass my five iron.'
2. 'I can throw it further than I can hit it.'
3. 'Which club should I use, a belter or a prodder?'

CHAPTER SIX

Caricatures

Gren has, over the years, been delighted to accept invitations to produce caricatures of the great, the good (and the frankly quite dopey) for press publications and for individuals to mark certain occasions such as promotion, retirement or in fact any personal highlight. As the latter are all hanging in boardrooms, offices, homes and pubs, we were unable to include them in this volume. However, the following are some caricatures that have appeared in the press.

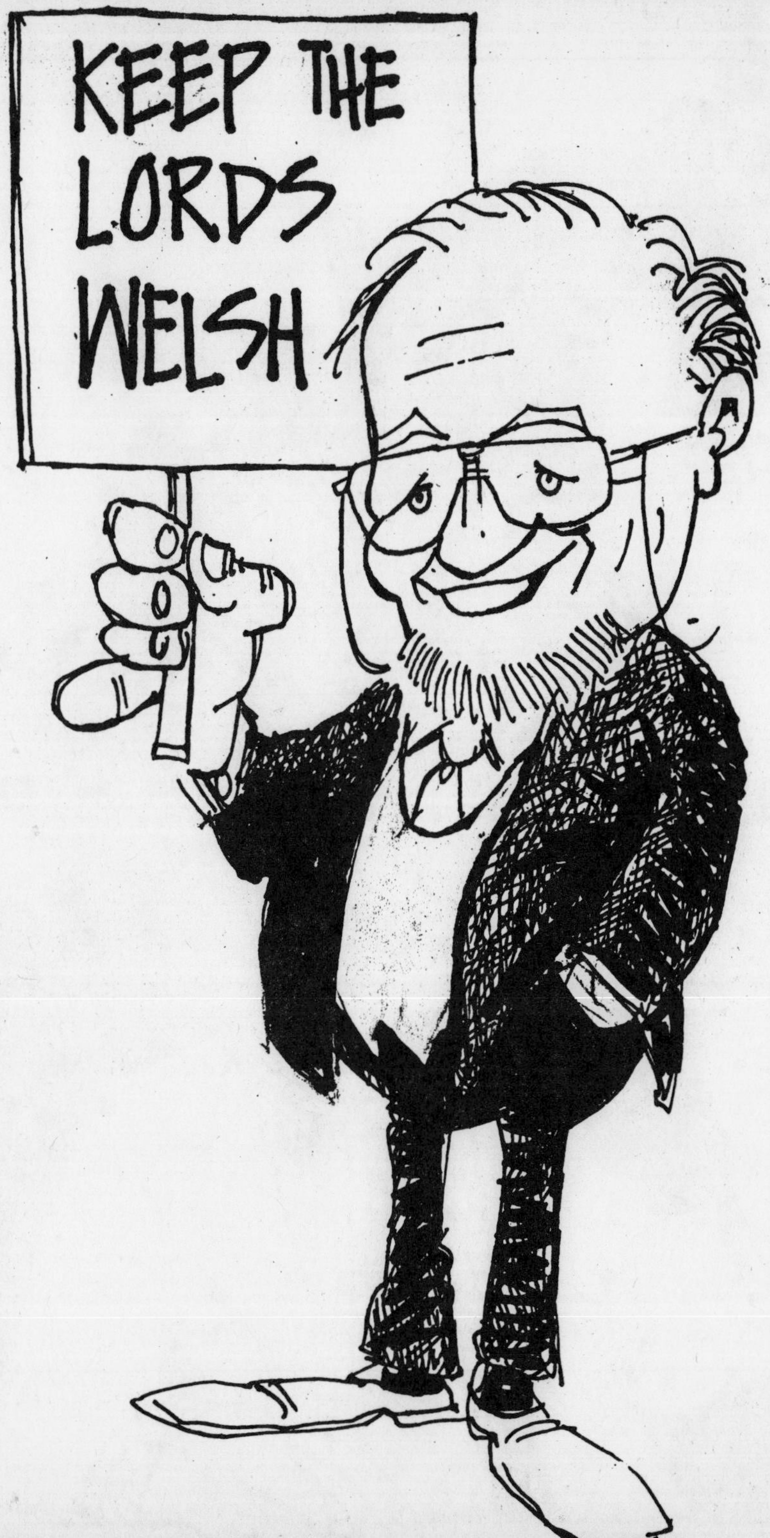
KEEP THE
LORDS
WELSH

Lord Gordon Parry, 20 March 1990.

Rhodri Morgan — First
Secretary, Welsh
Assembly.

Rt Hon John Redwood, when
Secretary of State for Wales.

Neil Jenkins —
Wales, Lions and
Baa-Baas' Cardiff
outside-half.

Menu cover drawing to commemorate Neil Kinnock's
20 years as MP for Islwyn.

Top toastmaster Harry Pooloway is honoured by the Toastmasters' Guild of Great Britain.

Sir Wyn Roberts, August 1990.

Dewi Griffiths, BBC. A presentation caricature upon his retirement.

'Geevers' — G.V. Wynne-Jones' 75th birthday presentation, 1988.

Top rugby writer J.B.G.
Thomas on his retirement,
May 1982.

Graham Price, Wales and Lions, from a menu cover, 1986.

Richard Stilgoe and Peter Skellern in 'Stilgoe & Skellern' for Lords Taverners, June 1990.

CHAPTER SEVEN

Noble Expressions

Noble Expressions is just one of the many books illustrated by Gren. Star broadcasting personality Roy Noble produced a delightful collection of love poems. The coupling of Roy's words and Gren's drawings resulted in a very enjoyable volume. Roy and Gren later combined to produce *Welsh Nicknames* for Western Mail Books.

I like the way your eyes give signs —
Like signals that I've seen:
Red is stop, and amber... well
I love it when they're green.

Like laver bread and bacon,
Like sand washed by the tide,
Like mushy peas and faggots,
We belong there — side by side.

You're like shampoo upon my dandruff,
You're like glasses to my eyes;
And when you say I'm handsome
I just love your kindly lies.

Those stolen moments coyly shared —
Recalled as if by knack —
As the usherette cried 'None of that,
Take your hand from 'neath your mac.'

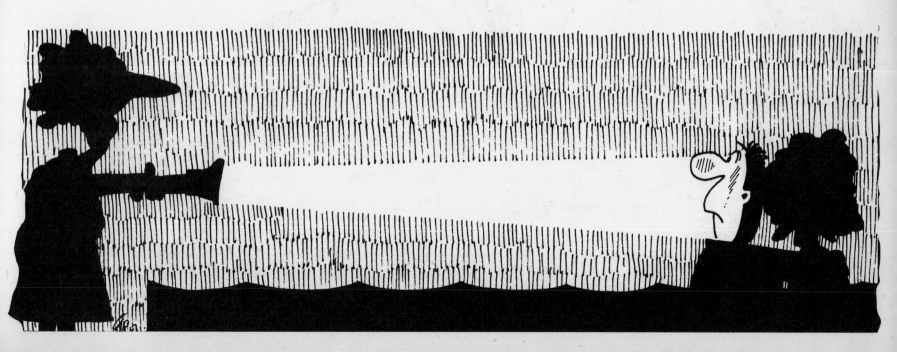

That lovely night in winter time
We felt the chill air's whiff;
We stuck our ground — in rays of love —
Although quite frozen stiff.

I couldn't do without you,
You're my strength when life gets rough;
Outwardly so very smooth,
But like brillo, pretty tough.

You're the flavour on my ice cream,
You're my cheese in fondue dips,
You're blancmange atop my jelly,
And vinegar on my chips.

You're the wine that flows in summer,
Like fine nectar, only sweeter;
You're the motive in my thinking,
You're the shilling in my meter.

Like the shrubs are in our border,
Like the spring-cleaned glass is clear,
Our love is like a flower —
A perennial through the year.

Like water 'bove my swimming trunks
You're the unexpected 'Hey!';
Like double strength white peppermints
You take my breath away.

You're image comes at strange odd times,
It wafts its way to wend;
Like when I was beneath the car
And noticed its big end.

You lighten up my day for me —
You guide me like a map;
You're the sweetener in my cup of tea,
And the butter on my bap.

The wind may blow,
    the rain may fall,
But I care not, not a jot.
To me it's always summer love
As our passion's always hot.

I love you more than anything,
To me you are much fairer
Than my hi-fi or my video
Or my Cosworth Ford Sierra.

Like a farmer needs a tractor;
Like a postman needs a bag;
You help me with each heavy load
And you lift me when I sag.

In life's long test your master mind
And love will ne'er diminish;
You ask how long my love will last
Well now I've started, so I'll finish.

Ah, my love, this public face
Hides what I feel beneath;
You make me smile so wide each day
Like toothpaste on my teeth.